The Llanthony warehouse in Gloucester Dock on the Gloucester and Sharpness Canal was extensively restored and opened in 1988 as the home of the National Waterways Museum.

CANAL ARCHITECTURE

Peter L. Smith

Shire Publications Ltd

CONTENTS

Printed in Great Britain by C. I. Thomas & Sons (Haverfordwest) Ltd, Press Buildings, Merlin Bridge, Haverfordwest, Dyfed SA61 1XF.

British Library Cataloguing in Publication Data. Smith, Peter L. Canal Architecture. — 2nd ed I. Title. 627.130941. ISBN 0-7478-0169-X.

ACKNOWLEDGEMENTS

Photographs on the following pages are acknowledged to: British Waterways Board Photo Library, title page; Audrey Chamberlain, page 28; Cadbury Lamb, cover and page 27 (lower); Robert V. May, page 17; Jeremy G. Simpson, page 10; R. M. Sinclair, page 23 (upper). The line illustrations on pages 4, 6 and 7 are by John W. Holroyd. The photograph on page 22 (upper) is from the author's collection, all other photographs are by the author.

COVER: *A canalside warehouse at Shardlow, Derbyshire.*

BELOW: *One of the best known of all canal structures, the Bingley Five Rise staircase locks on the Leeds and Liverpool Canal. The masonry work of the chambers, retaining walls and overflow weirs is exceptionally good.*

he Wrenbury Lift Bridge on the Llangollen Canal.

INTRODUCTION

he early canal engineers had to use all
ieir skill and ingenuity to succeed be-
iuse not only was the work they were
ɔing new but before 1801 they had no
rdnance Survey maps to rely on. The
igineers therefore had to make their
ʌn surveys and maps and in so doing
scover the different geological forma-
ɔns along their route, or else the con-
ructional problems could be consider-
ɔle. An eminent engineer usually had
ʌerall responsibility for the construction
ʾ a canal, with resident engineers to
ipervise the day to day work. Some of
e site engineers did more than that, for
ey also designed and built many canal
ɔmpany structures. On some projects
intractors were employed and they,
o, might be called upon to design and
ild small buildings. So structures with a
nilar purpose show a wide variety of
ɔsign.

James Brindley (1716-72), the first
eat canal engineer, had worked as a
millwright before his involvement with
the Bridgewater Canal in 1759. Afterwards he built an extensive network of
canals, being best known for his work on
the Trent and Mersey Canal and the
Staffordshire and Worcestershire Canal.
Many engineers were to follow Brindley,
including Benjamin Outram (1764-1805),
whose Derby and Peak Forest canals are
the most noteworthy; William Jessop
(1745-1814), whose greatest work was the
Grand Junction Canal extending from
the Midlands to London; and John Rennie (1761-1821), who also started work
with a millwright and is remembered for
his wide waterways like the Basingstoke,
Lancaster and Kennet and Avon canals.
One of the greatest canal engineers was
Thomas Telford (1757-1834), the son of a
shepherd from Dumfries. His greatest
achievements include the Shropshire Union Canal and the Caledonian Canal,
both notable for their directness.

3

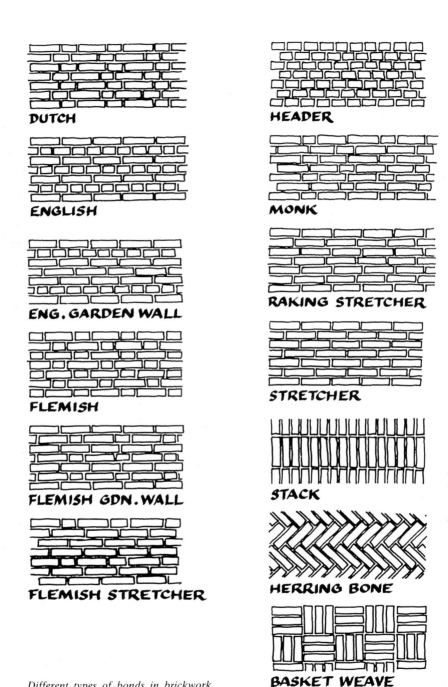

DUTCH

ENGLISH

ENG. GARDEN WALL

FLEMISH

FLEMISH GDN. WALL

FLEMISH STRETCHER

HEADER

MONK

RAKING STRETCHER

STRETCHER

STACK

HERRING BONE

BASKET WEAVE

Different types of bonds in brickwork.

4

..t Brentford on the Grand Union Canal is this brick building with a slate roof and ornamented ...himney. Built for use as a toll and traffic office it was considered worthy of decoration if only to ...crease its prestige.

BUILDING MATERIALS AND PRACTICES

...atural rock was the ideal building mate-...al for canals and vast quantities were ...sed, but bricks proved to be a good ...bstitute. Before the nineteenth century ...l the bricks were handmade, from ...arious coloured clays containing silica. ...arge quantities of timber, especially ...nglish oak, were used for making lock ...ates, piling wharves and building small ...ridges.

From the eighteenth century iron be-...an to be used in large quantities, espe-...ally for bridge construction. This ap-...ication gathered pace with further de-...elopments in the production of wrought ...on and, after 1855, steel.

In the 1820s, a Yorkshireman, Joseph ...spdin, invented an artificial cement that ... recognised as the basis of all modern ...oncrete. It was good in compression but ...oor in tension; however, the use of ...oncrete continued to increase. In 1865 ...oncrete reinforced with steel bars was ...troduced, and it has subsequently be-...ome one of the most important building ...aterials.

The type of brickwork in favour during the early years of the canal era was Flemish bond. This method involved laying courses made up of alternating heads and stretchers, that is with the long side of one brick exposed followed by another with only the end visible, in all cases avoiding a straight joint immediate-ly above another such joint in the course below. At first only plain rectangular bricks were available, which although satisfactory for most building work, left limited scope for decoration. When canal building got under way the use of ornate-ly shaped bricks had become common, but few were used in early canal struc-tures. If it was decided to incorporate a little decoration it was done with the bricks to hand, by making relief or raised brickwork in the form of squares, dia-monds, circles or crosses in the walls, similar to those on the portals of the Greywell Tunnel. On roofed buildings they often incorporated an ornamental feature under the eaves, resembling, for example, a row of teeth, made by placing

5

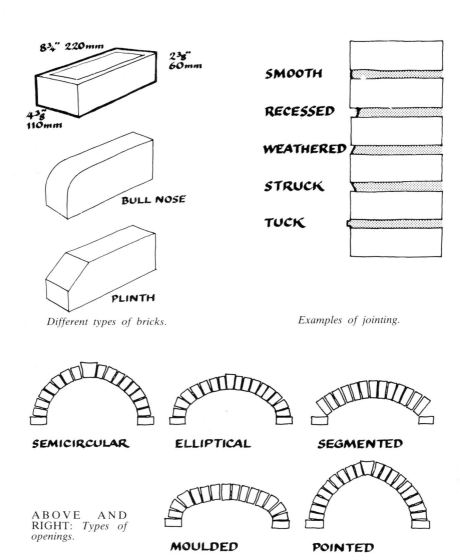

Different types of bricks.

Examples of jointing.

SMOOTH

RECESSED

WEATHERED

STRUCK

TUCK

SEMICIRCULAR

ELLIPTICAL

SEGMENTED

ABOVE AND RIGHT: *Types of openings.*

MOULDED

POINTED

a course of headers with alternating ones projecting, known as dentilation. Alternatively the bricks were laid diagonally to produce a serrated edge finish. Numerous examples of dentilation can be seen, such as on the Somerton Deep Lock cottage on the Oxford Canal, and the stables at Stockton Brook on the Caldon Canal.

On important buildings such as offices, where decoration was felt to be justified,

decorated bricks would be used in th facing, perhaps with properly moulde window mullions and transoms, and wit moulded doorway arches or ornament spandrels. Some incorporated elaborate ly moulded cornices to separate th storeys, as well as triangular pediments the apex of the gables. The chimne stacks were often made circular, octago al, hexagonal or even spiral-shaped, wit ornamental finishes. Many buildings i corporate some of these features, such as the toll office at Brentford on the Grand Union Canal and the canal office at Little Venice in London. Elaborate decoration was also common on many stone-clad brick buildings, for example the Sleaford Navigation Office in Sleaford, which is finished in limestone with an octagonal chimney, Gothic windows and a coat of arms over the main entrance.

Bricks required mortar to hold them together and the basis of this mortar was coarse sand, which for many years was mixed with slaked lime. Later cement, which gave a far stronger joint, was used instead of lime. Adding colour to the mortar often gives a building a pleasing appearance, as also can the way the individual joints are finished off. When the mortar is ½ inch (13 mm) or so thick this can be done, and a struck or weathered joint that throws off the rain may be practical, while a recessed or flashed joint can be most attractive.

On building sites where stone was used the work was done by masons, who were usually classed as banker or fixer masons. The banker masons were the hewers, the craftsmen who shaped the blocks of stone on benches. The fixer masons, who usually worked in teams, were concerned with the placing of the dressed stone. To place a stone of perhaps half a ton in weight into its final position a lifting device was necessary. So that none of the lifting gear passed underneath the stone

to disturb the building mortar, a lewis was used. It consisted of a shackle with three legs that fixed into a dovetail mortice cut into the centre of the stone block. Shearlegs erected as a tripod over the work area were used for most lifting work, and wooden jib cranes with geared winches for the larger tasks.

Cutting, dressing and carving the stone was skilful work done by masons who spent many years learning their trade. Each mason put his own special identification mark on each piece of work. Although the marks do not usually appear on exposed surfaces they can be seen on the stone blocks in many lock chambers, and around the western entrance to the Gannow tunnel at Burnley on the Leeds and Liverpool Canal.

If additional strength was deemed necessary to secure a stone, cramps and dowels were often used. Cramps are often found at locks, around the top of the chamber and near the gates, used to hold the large top stones in position and take some of the stress which the swinging gates impose on the masonry. The cramps are flat bars of iron with the ends bent over. To join the blocks together the ends of the cramps were bedded with lead into holes cut into the stone. The molten lead often spat and injured the men as it was poured on to the cold iron and stone. To overcome this, the hole with the cramp in position was first filled with molten wax, then as the lead was

RIGHT: *Masons' marks.*
BELOW: *A three-legged Lewis.*

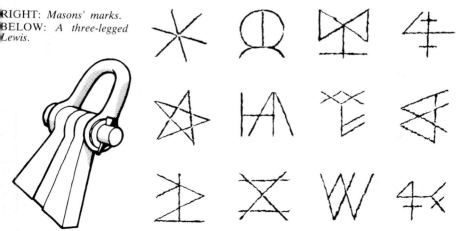

7

poured it replaced the wax without spitting.

Ashlar is masonry, usually limestone or sandstone of fine grain, that has been carefully dressed and squared and made smooth on the front and sides, to be used as facing material, with very fine-jointed level courses. Its use gave added refinement to a building. The horizontal joints in ashlar masonry are known as bed joints and the vertical joints as perpends. Another finish used on both large and small structures was 'rock facing', a coarse, lumpy finish similar to exposed weathered rock. The finished stonework on walling often looks best when left

plain, although there are many cases where tooling has improved the overall appearance. Tooling included rustication, which was simply recessing the joints either by chamfering or square edging, and vermiculation, which gave the stone the overall impression of being covered with winding worm tracks. Another finish was punched herring bone, which was achieved by cutting punched strokes diagonally from the two long edges of the block to give V-shaped markings. A splendid selection of tooling work can be seen on the Ladysmith Bridge on the Kennet and Avon Canal.

On the Rufford branch of the Leeds and Liverpool Canal is this well proportioned masonry bridge and lock. The paddle gearing and lock gate beams are typical of those found throughout this cross-country waterway.

LOCKS

There are about 1500 canal locks still in use in Britain. Known as pound locks, they made possible the canalisation of rivers and the construction of canals. The locks were needed to overcome differences in levels. The lock chambers were designed to allow passage of the largest craft on the canal, while using the minimum quantity of water. They are generally rectangular in shape but there are exceptions, like the one at Aynho on the Oxford Canal, which is diamond shape.

Most of the 'narrow' canals of the Midlands have locks with chambers 7 feet 2.1 m) wide and about 75 feet (22.9 m) long. They were built to accommodate a boat 6 feet 10 inches (2.03 m) wide and 70 feet (21 m) long, the extra length of the chamber allowing the bottom gates to swing open and closed. The operation of a lock is as simple as its basic design: by the use of paddle gearing a boat can be lifted or lowered between the two different water levels at the head and tail of the structure. The gearing at each end of the lock lifts and lowers vertical timber shutters, called paddles, seated in grooves at the end of sluices. This allows water to flow into the lock chamber from the

higher pound above when lifting a boat, or flow out of the chamber into the canal pound below to empty the lock and lower the boat. Each time it is used the average narrow lock allows about 25,000 gallons (114,000 litres) of water to pass from the higher to the lower canal level. A wide-beamed lock, with a chamber about 14 feet (4.3 m) wide or more, used for the passage of barges, transfers about twice as much water.

Locks are constructed either individually or in flights. Impressive flights can be seen at Delph Locks on the Dudley Canal; at Wigan, where twenty-three locks lift the Leeds and Liverpool Canal out of the town; at Cain Hill, Devizes, where seventeen locks are positioned in a straight line; at Tardebigge, with thirty-seven locks within 3 miles (5 km); at Hatton, near Warwick, with twenty-one wide locks; and at Wolverhampton, with the same number of narrow locks.

Lock construction incorporates many different types of gates and balance beams, side and overflow weirs, footbridges and walkways, chambers, bollards, paddle gearing, name and number

A canal scene typical of many on the southern Oxford Canal with a brick-built lock and keeper cottage alongside the lock.

10

plates. Side ponds that allow for the re-use of water are found on some canals. Lock gates are usually of timber, remaining watertight by constant immersion, but occasionally of iron or steel. Some lock chambers were cut out of solid rock, like the staircase locks in Chester, but most have chambers of brick, stone or a combination of both. Many brick chambers have been completely renewed, and for over one hundred years this has often been done with Staffordshire blue bricks, which resist damp. Many of these rebuilt chambers have been neatly finished off around the top edge with special blue bull-nosed bricks. A few chambers have been renewed with concrete or steel piling, often the result of resiting due to road construction, such as the bottom lock of the flight at Stoke-on-Trent.

Most canal locks have swinging gates, but there are exceptions, as at Kings Norton, where the lock at the junction of the northern Stratford Canal with the Worcester and Birmingham Canal has guillotine gates. There are guillotine gates at Salterhebble on a canal section of the Calder and Hebble Navigation.

The Bratch Locks on the Staffordshire and Worcestershire are standard pound locks positioned only a few feet apart, with just sufficient room for the gates to swing. The water in the short intermediate pounds flows through culverts to storage areas nearby. The locks mark a stage in the evolution of locks, for they are nearly, but not quite, staircase locks. Staircase locks came to be built when a steep hillside had to be overcome by a canal. Then a number of locks were joined together, the top gate(s) of one chamber also acting as the bottom gate(s) of the chamber above. The most famous staircase locks are John Longbottom's Bingley Five Rise on the Leeds and Liverpool Canal. These locks, complete with five massive masonry chambers, have enormous intermediate gates; altogether the flight has a total lift of 60 feet (18.2 m). On the Leicester section of the Grand Union Canal at Foxton there are two sets of five locks that have one intermediate pound for boats to pass. On the Caledonian Canal are the huge stone-built Muirtown, Fort Augustus and Bana-

The flight of narrow locks and overflow weirs at Delph on the Birmingham Canal Navigations. Now part of a conservation area, the lock surroundings have been much improved.

vie staircase locks, consisting of four, five and eight chambers respectively. There are many other examples of staircase locks elsewhere.

Inclined planes and lifts were used on some canals to overcome differences in levels. Few were made and even fewer have survived. One that has, the Anderton Lift, was constructed in 1875 to connect the Trent and Mersey Canal with the river Weaver in Cheshire. Converted from a hydraulic mechanism to electricity in 1906-7, the lift has two caissons, each 75 feet (22.9 m) long and 15 feet 6 inches (4.7 m) wide, suspended by wire ropes from an overhead arrangement of cogs,

pulleys and counterweights. Independently operated, each caisson is capable of holding a pair of narrow boats and is raised and lowered 50 feet (15.2 m) between the river and the canal. Another survivor is the Hay Inclined Plane at Coalport, last used in 1894 to lift and lower tub boats that travelled on cradles running on railway lines. The weight of the descending cradle helped to pull the loaded one. At each end of the incline the boats were floated off the cradles to continue their journey by water. The remains of other inclined planes exist, such as Foxton and on the closed Bude Canal in Cornwall.

A view of the Stanley Ferry Aqueduct, which shows clearly its classical design.

The Engine Branch of the Birmingham Canal Navigations is carried across the main line by this graceful Telford aqueduct.

AQUEDUCTS

The first aqueduct built in Britain for navigation was the Barton aqueduct, which carried the Bridgewater Canal across the river Irwell and so enabled it to reach Salford. At first the idea was ridiculed, but when completed its builder, James Brindley, was acclaimed. The three-arched stone aqueduct and its approaches totalled 600 feet (183 m) in length. It was opened in 1761 and remained in use until 1893, when it was replaced by a unique swinging aqueduct when the river Irwell below became part of the Manchester Ship Canal.

Afterwards Brindley was to build a number of similar aqueducts, a design which did not change much for over a quarter of a century. Because of the immense weight of the water and the thick layer of clay puddle, which was laid in the masonry trough to stop water leaking into the stonework, these first aqueducts were of a squat appearance, and mostly with a succession of low arches. Typical are the Dove Aqueduct which Brindley made to carry the Trent

and Mersey Canal over the river at Clay Mills in Staffordshire, and two on the northern section of the Staffordshire and Worcestershire Canal that carry the canal over the rivers Trent and Sow.

A notable development in aqueduct design was the Lea Wood masonry aqueduct on the Cromford Canal, opened in August 1794. Built with just one arch of 80 feet (24.38 m) span and 30 feet (9.14 m) high, it was the forerunner of much greater structures, such as the Lune Aqueduct near Lancaster on the Lancaster Canal. The canal was built by John Rennie, but the aqueduct was largely designed by the Scottish architect and civil engineer Alexander Stevens. It took four years to build and was completed in 1797. The magnificent structure of rockfaced millstone grit has five identical arches, each with a 70 foot (21 m) span. The aqueduct has a total length of 664 feet (202 m) and is notable for its attractive proportions, ornate balustrades and elegant cornices.

The Marple Aqueduct is best seen

either from the river banks 100 feet (30 m) below or from the railway viaduct alongside. Built by Benjamin Outram, this awe-inspiring structure carries the Peak Forest Canal over the river Goyt. Completed in 1802, the masonry spandrels are pierced with cylindrical cut-outs made to lighten the structure and to enable wide arches to be made that allow for the unrestricted flow of flood water. Rennie designed many beautiful structures and two of his best are the Dundas and Avoncliffe aqueducts which carry the Kennet and Avon Canal over the Bristol Avon. Built of Bath stone, they are splendid examples of Georgian architecture.

In 1795, after Josiah Clowes, the engineer who was building a masonry aqueduct at Longdon upon Tern, on the Shrewsbury Canal, had died, Thomas Telford was appointed to succeed him. By that time the partly built aqueduct had been mostly washed away by floods. Telford was aware of the developments in the use of iron in construction work and designed an aqueduct using this material. It was fabricated at the Ketley works of William Reynolds and erected on site using the remains of the original sandstone abutments. The trough of the aqueduct was basically a great beam made up of cast iron sections and supported on vertical and diagonal struts. This aqueduct, 186 feet (56.69 m) in length, was opened in March 1796, but it was not the first iron aqueduct for a canal. One designed by Benjamin Outram was opened one month before Telford's at The Holmes in Derby. Outram's aqueduct had a single span to carry the Derby Canal over a small tributary of the river Derwent, but no longer exists. Though disused the Longdon upon Tern aqueduct survives.

At about the same time, on what is now known as the Llangollen Canal, a masonry aqueduct was being constructed at Chirk to carry the canal over the Ceiriog. It was decided to fit a cast iron plate in the bottom of the trough instead of using clay puddle. Opened in 1801, the completed aqueduct, 600 feet (183 m) in length and with ten arches and hollow spandrels, was 70 feet (21 m) high. 4 miles (6 km) further along the same canal at Pontcysyllte, it had been planned to drop down the valley with locks and cross over the river Dee by another much smaller aqueduct. Then it was decided to erect an iron aqueduct instead. A foundation stone was laid on 25th July 1795 and when completed, in 1805, the 1007 foot (306.9 m) aqueduct was the wonder of the age, being the highest and longest navigable aqueduct in Britain. The trough, 126 feet (38.43 m) above the river at the highest point, is carried on nineteen arches, also of iron and each with a span of 45 feet (13.7 m),

ABOVE: The brick-built Hazelhurst 'fly-over' aqueduct that carries one sec-. tion of the Caldon Canal over another.

RIGHT: Pontcysyllte Aqueduct, with its iron trough and arches, sits on slim masonry piers and carries the Llangollen Canal over the Dee valley.

which stand on slender masonry piers.

The building of iron aqueducts continued; Telford designed many, including two on the Shropshire Union Canal. One crosses the A5 road at Stretton, the other the A51 at Nantwich. Rennie also used iron and his best aqueduct is at Wolverhampton on the Grand Union (formerly Grand Junction) Canal, completed in 1809. George Leather Junior (1787-1870) built the Stanley Ferry aqueduct near Wakefield, to carry a canal section of the Aire and Calder Navigation over the river Calder. Completed in 1839, it consists of two parallel cast iron arches each weighing 101 tons, with a 165 foot (50.32 m) span and a trough 180 feet (55 m) long, holding 940 tons of water, suspended between them. The new Barton aqueduct, completed in 1893, is a movable structure that revolves on a central pier, with a trough 18 feet (5.5 m) wide and 7 feet (2.1 m) deep and holding 800 tons of water.

Bricks were used for some major aqueducts during the later days of the canal age, when improvements and changes were being made to some of the original routes, such as on the Birmingham Canal Navigations. Many of these brick aqueducts are 'fly-overs', built near canal junctions to carry one section of canal over another. One of the finest is the Hazelhurst aqueduct which carries the Leek branch of the Caldon Canal over the section to Froghall. Aqueducts of reinforced concrete have been built in recent years, for example, where the Tame Valley Canal of the Birmingham Canal Navigations passes over the M5 motorway at West Bromwich and Dudley Port. At Stanley Ferry a new prestressed concrete aqueduct was opened in 1981 alongside the older unique iron structure, which had been damaged by mining subsidence.

LEFT: *A section of the Marple Aqueduct, showing one of the pierced cylindrical cut-outs in the spandrel that made it possible to have wide arches.*
RIGHT: *Built of masonry, the Marple flight of locks on the Peak Forest Canal is crossed by several roads. To speed the movement of men and horses a number of small tunnels were made: this one was intended for the horse, hence the rope marks (lower left).*

The Birmingham Canal Navigations' main line is crossed by Telford's Galton Bridge, which is 75 feet (22.85 m) high.

BRIDGES

When the canals were built, they intersected many roads and other rights of way, so bridges had to be constructed to take these over the canals. Other bridges, known as accommodation bridges, were required to enable farmers to move livestock and for property owners to gain access to their land. To appease rich landowners living in large houses near the canal, companies often built ornate bridges, some with balustrades and statues, to carry approach roads. Examples can be seen on many canals, but one of the most impressive is the one over the Grand Union at Cassiobury Park, Watford.

Many of the original bridges have survived unchanged. Some have humped backs and others carry level or even sloping roadways. The simplest bridges have a semicircular or segmented arch that was formed to carry a heavy superimposed weight. The arches consist of an arrangement of bricks or stones built in a curve with all the joints pointing to a centre and so support one another by mutual pressure, with all the weight perpetually transferred down through each wedge-shaped voussoir to the springings and abutments.

In 1800 two iron footbridges made by the Coalbrookdale Company were erected over the Kennet and Avon Canal in Bath. Shortly afterwards a local company, Stotherts, supplied a further two iron bridges. In many parts of Britain new ironworks made bridges: in the London area, for example, bridges were supplied by local firms such as Henry Grissell and R. Masefield and Company,

A well made cast iron bridge with masonry abutments over the Leeds and Liverpool Canal in Liverpool.

of Chelsea. One type of small iron bridge, principally erected on the southern Stratford Canal, consists of two arms cantilevered from the bridge abutments, leaving a central gap through which the tow lines would pass. Examples of this type of bridge can also be seen on the southern end of the Staffordshire and Worcestershire Canal. Because of the extensive use of tow ropes, excessive wear soon showed on the corners of many bridge abutments. To overcome this, iron guard plates were fitted on many bridges, where grooves made by the ropes can still be seen.

Telford built many iron bridges over rivers and canals. Galton Bridge, erected in 1829 over a cutting on the new main

Built across a sweeping curve of the Grand Union Canal is bridge number 164. This decorated bridge with a well proportioned balustrade and pedestrian tunnels is at Cassiobury Park, Watford.

18

An early single-arched humped-back masonry bridge built without a towpath.

A masonry turn-over bridge on the Macclesfield Canal in use as it was originally intended, with a horse passing over and the towing line still connected.

Macclesfield Bridge in Regent's Park is set on Coalbrookdale cast iron columns. Accidentally blown up in 1874, the bridge was rebuilt using the original columns, which were re-erected facing the wrong way; the tow line abrasions prove this.

line of the Birmingham Canal Navigations, is one of the finest, with a span of 150 feet (45.75 m) at a height of 75 feet (22.85 m). The Horseley Iron Works, which supplied the castings for the Galton Bridge, for over half a century made well designed and graceful towpath bridges. Many of these, some designed by William Cubitt, can be seen on the northern Oxford Canal and the Birmingham Canal Navigations. The towpath bridges were built to carry the towpath over canal junctions, arms and basin entrances, allowing the horses to proceed without having to unhitch the tow ropes. The need to keep the horse moving was the prime consideration in the design of 'roving' or 'turn-over' bridges, which were built where the towpath changed from one side of the canal to the other. Mostly with sweeping curved lines, some of the best masonry examples can be seen on the Macclesfield Canal.

Some canal bridges are movable, like the bascule types, evolved from draw-bridges. These are opened by pulling on a chain or using a winch. Many can be seen on the Llangollen and Caldon canals, the Northampton and Welford arms of the Grand Union and the northern Stratford Canal. On other canals swing bridges were erected. Most carry a country road and they usually have a wooden deck which is pivoted on a turntable alongside the canal. There are many on the Leeds and Liverpool Canal, with others on the Upper Peak Forest, Lancaster, Macclesfield, Pocklington, Grand Union, Kennet and Avon, and Stainforth and Keadby Canals. All the bridges on the New Junction Canal were at first manually operated swing bridges, but in the 1970s they were changed and now are a mixture of large electrically operated lift and swing bridges. The Gloucester and Sharpness Canal is another where all the bridges are of the movable type. They include both lift and swing examples, and because some carry busy roads these are electrically operated.

Crossing the Shropshire Union Canal's deep cuttings are some bridges that are three or four times the height of normal bridges. This double-arched bridge is of interest because it includes some wooden remains.

One of the bridge keepers' cottages on the Gloucester and Sharpness Canal, built in the classical Regency style complete with a pedimented portico on Doric columns.

CANALSIDE BUILDINGS

Most early canal buildings were purely functional, and workers' cottages were usually built of the same material and to the same basic plan as the local rural dwellings. But there were exceptions, like the brick-built round houses on the Staffordshire and Worcestershire Canal. One with a castellated top can be seen at Gailey, where the A5 road crosses the canal. Similar houses dating from 1799, but of stone rendered with plaster and stucco, can be seen at a few places on the route of the closed Thames and Severn Canal. Six examples of another unusual type of early canal cottage remain on the southern Stratford Canal between Lapworth and Preston Bagot. These are single-storey cottages built with a barrel-shaped roof. Later some very elaborate structures were built, with certain canal companies adopting specific standard designs. The Shropshire Union Canal, for example, built many fine-looking houses and bungalows of the same basic design, having observation porches, with a low roof jutting out over bay windows on wide eaves. Some of the most elaborate cottages are on the Gloucester and Sharpness Canal. In a Regency style,

each has a pedimented portico on Doric columns.

Much larger houses for managers, agents and engineers were also built. One such brick-built house stands facing the Kings Norton Junction on the Worcester and Birmingham Canal. Another large brick-built house, with a broad central bay and curved verandah, and with wide eaves for the overhanging slate roof, is situated alongside the top of the Grindley Brook flight of locks on the Llangollen Canal. An engineer once lived in the Junction House at Marple, where the Macclesfield Canal joins the Peak Forest Canal.

The earliest canalside public houses were simple structures with steeply pitched roofs and casement windows, like the worker's cottages but larger. They were used as gathering places providing both refreshment and information for the boat people, and where deals were struck over the carriage of goods for local farmers and business people. In addition, because stables were located in many pub yards, boat-hauling arrangements could be agreed with the horse owners. Innumerable pubs were built by canal companies

21

ABOVE: *Built by a local contractor, the Chalford Round House on the former Thames and Severn Canal dates from 1799. Five of these structures of stone rendered with plaster and stucco were originally built.*

LEFT: *Photographed from the A5 road, the round house at Gailey on the Staffordshire and Worcestershire Canal is an interesting building, the otherwise plain walls being castellated.*

Ladywood Lock cottage on the Droitwich Canal. This building collapsed in 1980 but was completely rebuilt by the Canal Trust to be used as a holiday home. Elsewhere on the canal network, cottages are being given a new lease of life as holiday centres.

and others wherever the need arose to serve the canal community, at canal junctions, beside humped-back bridges, alongside locks and basins and near wharves and warehouses. They were usually given a canal-linked name, such as the Navigation, the Boat, the Canal Tavern or the Bridge Inn. Examples are the Eight Locks, alongside the Ryders

Green Locks at Walsall, the Two Boats at Long Itchington on the Grand Union, the Big Lock at Middlewich and the Swan at Fradley Junction, both on the Trent and Mersey Canal.

Larger properties were built as hotels, which were often used as staging points for the packet boat services. Many such hotels had large banqueting halls and

On the southern Stratford Canal there are six of these cottages that were constructed by a local contractor. Built in the form of a single-arched bridge with brick walls to seal the ends, these cottages are both pleasant and unusual.

ABOVE: *Brick-built warehouses at Wigan on the Leeds and Liverpool Canal. Empty and derelict for many years, under the urban aid programme they are being restored in an imaginative fashion to conserve the waterways heritage and provide the focal point for new leisure and tourism ventures.* BELOW: *The splendid Gauxholme warehouse on the Rochdale Canal, with its arched barge entry, was designed to cater for a high volume of canal traffic.*

ere regularly used by the canal companies for directors' meetings. An example is the Georgian-style Tontine at ourport, built alongside the canal asins, with the front overlooking the ver Severn. Another hotel regularly sed for directors' meetings and where acket boat passengers stayed was The owther, a large square brick-built building with stone ornamentation, near the ocks in Goole.

As arteries of transport the canals enerated trade, and numerous warehouses were built, some with wide arches o allow the boats to be loaded under over. They were built of brick, stone or mber, with iron used in many warehouses for such items as pillars, beams nd for hand cranes. Wharves for anshipment and distribution were built, s well as offices and stables, many with rrounding yards, cobbled or paved ith brick or granite setts. The concenation of activities gave rise to a number inland ports. One of the first was ardlow, near Derby, on the Trent and lersey Canal, where many fine old nal buildings exist. Other handsome arehouses can still be seen at other rmer inland ports such as Sheffield and oventry. There are fine stone warehouses alongside the Sowerby Bridge asin, a former busy transhipment point here the Rochdale Canal connects with e Calder and Hebble Navigation. At Gloucester, which is still a busy port at the end of the Gloucester and Sharpness Canal, can be seen many large and well proportioned brick warehouses.

The towns of Stourport and Goole owe their existence to the canals that were made to connect with the local rivers. It was the joining of the Staffordshire and Worcestershire Canal with the river Severn that made Stourport, and in this late eighteenth-century town can be seen many buildings erected at that time, including a warehouse of warm mellow brick, enhanced by a clock tower. Goole was chosen as the connecting point between the tidal waters of the Ouse and the Knottingley and Goole Canal, and after 1826 as the canal flourished so did the fortunes of the new town and port, where even the hospital, church and schools were built mostly with money made from canal transport. Ellesmere Port is another canal town, the result of the Shropshire Union Canal being connected with the Manchester Ship Canal. Most of the remaining canal basins and buildings, amongst which are warehouses, toll office and stables, are now used to house the Boat Museum.

Smaller communities dependent upon water transport grew up at many other inland places that had previously relied upon agriculture, such as Thorne on the Stainforth and Keadby Canal and Braunston at the junction of the Oxford and

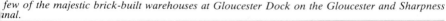

few of the majestic brick-built warehouses at Gloucester Dock on the Gloucester and Sharpness nal.

LEFT: *Maintenance yards owned by canal companies were usually built in a grand manner. The one at Bulbourne on the Grand Union Canal incorporates this impressive Italianate tower.*

BELOW: *A well designed and soundly constructed cover for a dry dock. Alongside the Marsworth Top Lock this mellow yellow-brick building with a slate roof is still used as it was originally intended.*

ABOVE: *At Stoke Bruerne on the Grand Union Canal this former canalside mill has found a new lease of life as the Canal Museum (previously known as the Waterways Museum). Alongside it, former canal company houses are now used mostly to house tourist businesses.*

BELOW: *The Iron Shed at the Ellesmere Port Boat Museum has been renovated to house craft workshops.*

Alongside the Staffordshire and Worcestershire Canal at Stourport is this brick building with metal window frames. Similar structures were erected at many places for various uses ranging from storage of goods to workshops.

Grand Union Canals. At both places the making of the first wharf was followed by further canal buildings, leading to a concentration of boatbuilding and repair activities that continues. The junction of the Coventry Canal and the Trent and Mersey was made some distance from the village of Fradley, but the building of a warehouse, stables, public house, canal repair yard and cottages resulted in a community isolated and independent from the village by both distance and livelihood.

Boatbuilding and repair work was undertaken at many places, where usually a dry dock was the centre of activities. The dry docks were fitted with gates and sluices to enable boats to be floated in and out. Many were open to the elements, while others were roofed over. At Stone on the Trent and Mersey Canal are examples of docks roofed over with both open and closed sides. At Marsworth on

the Grand Union Canal is a dry dock enclosed within a large brick building with a slate roof that has many louvred windows to assist ventilation.

Excellent repair and maintenance facilities, involving many different trades, were essential for the upkeep of a canal. Often the activities were concentrated in a canal repair workshop. Many of these are still fulfilling this role, including the workshops of the former Weaver Navigation at Northwich, where in addition to large work areas and spacious offices there is an elegant free-standing clock tower with a cupola. There is another clock tower at the Bulbourne workshops on the Grand Union, situated to one side of the main building. The Italian-style tower is enhanced by a semicircular fanlight over the entrance door. On the Coventry Canal are the brick-built Hartshill workshops, also with a clock tower and with

Numerous small buildings were erected alongside the canals for various purposes. This splendid example, used as a banksman's lobby, exists on the Staffordshire and Worcestershire Canal near Great Haywood Junction.

many semicircular windows and alcoves around the main building, which has a large archway entrance for boats from the canal.

For nearly two centuries thousands of horses daily trod the towpaths of Britain. To enable them to be fed, watered and rested many hundreds of stables were built by the canal companies and private owners. The stables owned by the canal companies were located near junctions, flights of locks, tunnels, warehouses and wharves. They were usually single-storey buildings with few windows but many doors, examples can be seen alongside the Bunbury locks on the Shropshire Union Canal, near the top of the Delph flight of locks and at Stockton Brook locks on the Caldon Canal. A few larger and more impressive stable blocks, with overhead hay lofts, tackle room and loose-box for sick animals, were built. One such stable block, finished in rock walling masonry, stands by the Dewsbury Basin of the Calder and Hebble Navigation. Built by the Aire and Calder Navigation in the 1860s, with its own blacksmiths' shop, the building is far superior to most of its counterparts.

Some of the smallest buildings erected were the toll offfices and lock-keepers lobbies. The lobbies, positioned on the lock sides to provide protection from the weather, were mostly simply constructed buildings of brick with a tile roof. A few unusual ones, circular in shape, with a chimney protruding from the top of a small domed roof, exist on the northern end of the Shropshire Union Canal. The toll offices, where the boatmen paid their dues for journeys, varied considerably in shape. Mostly built of brick, some were very plain while others were elaborate with ornamented chimneys, wide eaves dentilation and elegant windows and doorways, such as can be seen at Brentford. Some of the toll offices of the Staffordshire and Worcestershire Canal still exist. Alongside the York Street Lock in Stourport is one with a bay window while at Bratch and Stewponey Wharf are two octagonal ones, made of brick, with steep roofs to match the shape of the building.

Some of the largest buildings constructed were the pump houses, usually situated on the summit pound of the canal. Most were built to house steam powered beam engines to provide water for the canal from a nearby river; others oused pumps powered by waterwheels. On the Kennet and Avon Canal there is a ump house of each type. The one at 'rofton is a plain brick structure with a ıll chimney alongside. It contains a ıagnificent beam engine that can be seen orking on occasions. On the Wendover rm of the Grand Union is a far more npressive pump house with semicircular rched windows. One of the finest pump ouses is at Lea Wood on the Cromford 'anal. Built of millstone grit, it is nished in rock walling with ashlar dres- ıng, the two contrasting finishes of the ough and the smooth being done in the est masonry practice. This pump house longside the canal in a wooded valley as constructed to undertake a specific ractical function. Now it and the nearby queduct and wharf enhance the land- :ape, typical of many canal structures ıat are architectural gems in their own ght.

IGHT: *The Pump House at High Peak unction on the Cromford Canal in Derbyshire ; part of an interesting canal landscape, with everal architectural gems nearby, including an queduct, rail/water transhipment warehouse nd a cottage.*

ELOW: *A cast iron split bridge leaving a entral gap through which the tow line would ass.*

FURTHER READING

De Mare, Eric. *Bridges of Britain*. B. T. Batsford, 1975.
Gladwin, D. D. *A Pictorial History of Canals*. B. T. Batsford, 1976.
Harris, Robert. *Canals and Their Architecture*. Hugh Evelyn, 1969.
McKnight, Hugh. *The Shell Book of Inland Waterways*. David and Charles, 1975.
Pratt, Frances. *Canal Architecture in Britain*. British Waterways Board, 1976.
Smith, Peter L. *Discovering Canals in Britain*. Shire Publications, third edition 1989.

PLACES TO VISIT

The places listed below, with their grid references, are particularly worthy of a visit. In a
cases exploration of the local towpath is recommended, for there is a wealth of interest to b
found locally. In addition, exploration of the canal through most large cities will be foun
rewarding, as well as through the following towns: Bath, Bingley, Blackburn, Brighous
Burnley, Ellesmere Port, Falkirk, Hebden Bridge, Market Harborough, Middlewicl
Skipton, Stone, Stourport, Thorne, Trowbridge, Whaley Bridge, Wigan and Wolverhamj
ton

Anderton Lift, Cheshire (SJ 648753).
Barton Swing Aqueduct, Greater Manchester (SJ 767976).
Blisworth Tunnel, Northamptonshire (south entrance, SP 739503).
Braunston, Northamptonshire (SP 539658).
Chirk Tunnel and Aqueduct, Clwyd (SJ 285374).
Claverton Pump House, Avon (ST 791643).
Crofton Pump House, Wiltshire (SU 264626).
Delph Locks, West Midlands (SP 918865).
Devizes Locks, Wiltshire (Cain Hill Flight, SU 985615).
Dudley Tunnel, West Midlands (SO 942910).
Dundas Aqueduct, Avon (ST 784625).
Foxton Locks, Leicestershire (SP 692896).
Fradley Junction, Staffordshire (SK 141140).
Great Haywood Junction, Staffordshire (SJ 995229).
Harecastle Tunnel, Staffordshire (SJ 844528).
Hatton Flight, Warwickshire (top lock, SP 241669).
Hazelhurst Junction, Staffordshire (SJ 954537).
Kings Norton Junction, West Midlands (SP 053793).
Kingswood Junction, Warwickshire (SP 187718).
Lea Wood Pump House and Aqueduct, Derbyshire (SK 316557).
Longdon upon Tern Aqueduct, Shropshire (SO 483639).
Marple Aqueduct and Flight, Greater Manchester (SJ 962884).
Neptune Staircase, Banavie, Highland (NN 115772).
Netherton Tunnel, West Midlands (SP 953884).
Pontcysyllte Aqueduct, Clwyd (SJ 271420).
Sowerby Bridge Basin, West Yorkshire (SE 072236).
Stanley Ferry Aqueduct, West Yorkshire (SE 355231).
Stoke Bruerne, Northamptonshire (SP 739502).